# DEPRESSED CAT
## NINE MISERABLE LIVES

OH. THE. JOY.

# Depressed Cat: Nine Miserable Lives

Published by My Cardboard Books
Printed in Birmingham, UK
ISBN : 978-0-9568442-1-7

Fan artwork gallery pages 69-75 remain copyright of each individual artist, credits clockwise on each page: Howard Hardiman, Joseph Birdsong, Deanne Brady, Darryl Cunningham, Timothy Winchester, Greg McLeod, Soju Tanaka, Jim Medway, Paul Shinn, Eight Bit, David O'Connell, Gemma Correll, Stefan Dinter, Philippa Rice, Adam Cadwell, Elephant, Skilla Alliks, Francesca Cassavetti, Clara Roethe, Julia Scheele, Kayla Hillier, Myles McLeod, John McCrea, Clara, Madeleine Flores, Hunt Emerson, Tom Humberstone, Laurie Pink. Thanks to all! See website for links, full colour versions + More!

# SPRING

# DEPRESSED CAT'S BIRTHDAY

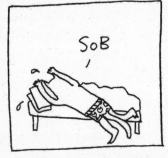

Depressed Cat
on Valentines day...
Sigh
At work
like any
other
day

# DEPRESSED CAT'S EVENING OUT...

Depressed cat eats dinner.

Depressed Cat "At the opticians"

# Depressed cat at a festival.

# Woke up with cat flu

# DEPRESSED CAT AROUND THE WORLD

# Depressed Cat enjoys summer in the UK!

Depressed cat at the car wash

# Depressed Cat "At the Supermarket"

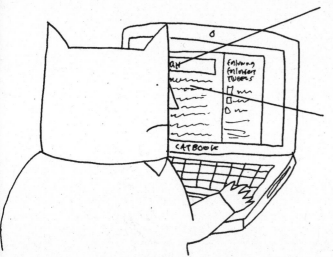

# Depressed Cat "At Disneyland..."

Gloom    Doom    Despair    Malaise

Misery    Distress    "The blues"    Forboding

The many faces of Depressed Cat. Tune in next week for anguish, cheerlessness, dejection, dismay, pessimism, pensiveness and low spirits.

Depressed Cat on the escalators

Wallowing in self pity and disgust.

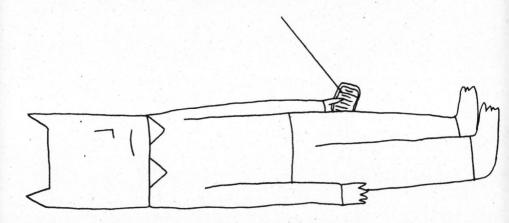

# DEPRESSED CAT'S CHILDHOOD YEARS.

AGE 0

AGE 1

AGE 2

AGED 3

AGE 4

AGE 5

Lizz likes boglins, board games and novelty Sellotape.
Read more comics at LizzLizz.COM